Raintree is an imprint of Capstone Global
Library Limited, a company incorporated in
England and Wales having its registered office
at 264 Banbury Road, Oxford, OX2 7DY –
Registered company number: 6695582

www.raintree.co.uk
myorders@raintree.co.uk

Editorial: Chris Harbo and Gena Chester
Design: Hilary Wacholz
Production: Kris Wilfahrt
Originated by Capstone Global Library Ltd
Printed and bound in India

Superman created by Jerry Siegel and Joe
Shuster. By special arrangement with the
Jerry Siegel family.

ISBN 978 1 4747 6663 0
22 21 20 19 18
10 9 8 7 6 5 4 3 2 1

British Library Cataloguing in Publication Data
A full catalogue record for this book is available
from the British Library.

RUFF RUFF!

BARK BARK!

League vs. Legion!

BY ART BALTAZAR AND FRANCO

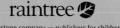
raintree
a Capstone company — publishers for children

MEANWHILE, IN THE PACIFIC OCEAN...

OUTRAGEOUSLY UNACCEPTABLE!

WHO DARES BUILD AN EVIL FORTRESS UPON MY OCEAN'S SURFACE?!

DISGUSTING!

THIS PERPETRATOR SHALL SUFFER THE WRATH OF...

BLACK MANTA!

WHILE ON **NEW KRYPTON**...

WHAT HAVE YOU DONE TO **JOR-EL**?

HA! YOU FOOL!

JOR-EL IS GONE!

THE CITY OF **KANDOR** NEEDS A LEADER.

WITH JOR-EL GONE...

ZOD

JOR-EL

BRAINIAC

ZOD

...I SHALL **RULE** NEW KRYPTON!

WE ARE THE SAME... ME AND YOU!

SAME GREEN SKIN.

SAME SYMBOL ON OUR FOREHEADS.

SAME TECHNOLOGY.

TECHNOLOGY?

THE SAME TECHNOLOGY CREATED US. IT'S FLOWING THROUGH OUR VEINS!

I'M NOT A ROBOT!

I KNOW!

AND THAT IS THE BEAUTY OF IT!

LET'S GO, PRYM-EL!

WE'RE LATE FOR OUR LEGION OF DOOM MEETING!

WAIT! NO! PRYM-EL, DON'T GO!

THE LEGION OF DOOM ARE EVIL!

SAY GOOD-BYE, PRYM-EL.

ZZZZORRMM

GOOD-BYE, PRYM-EL.

MMRZZWAH!!

WE MUST BE CAREFUL! PRYM-EL CAN BE INFLUENCED BY BRAINIAC VERY EASILY!

WE NEED ANSWERS!

WHAT ARE WE GOING TO DO?

WE MUST FLY TO EARTH!

TO THE ONLY PLACE I CAN TRUST WITH THE TRUTH!

THE FORTRESS OF SOLITUDE!

11

WHAT IS IT WITH YOU, **SQUIRREL**?

WHERE'S **HAL JORDAN**?

OR EVEN **JOHN STEWART**?

WE'RE TRYING SOMETHING DIFFERENT THIS TIME!

THERE'S ALWAYS ROOM IN THE **JUSTICE LEAGUE** FOR ANOTHER **GREEN LANTERN**...

...AND **I'M** THE GUY!

BUT...

...YOU'RE A SQUIRREL!

CURSES!

COLD!

FREEZE!

RUN!

FAST

RUN!

OW!

CURSES!

RIDDLE ME THIS, MY POINTY-EARED--

--AHK!

HMM... WHY ISN'T BRAINIAC ATTACKING?

OKAY, LUTHOR. IT'S TIME TO LEAVE!

SO SOON?

OUR NEWEST MEMBER SHOULD BE HERE ANY MINUTE NOW!

OH, LOOK!

THERE HE IS!

WHAT ON EARTH?!

IT'S NOT OF THIS WORLD!

LET ME INTRODUCE...

...STARRO!

THE ONE WHO WILL DESTROY THE **JUSTICE LEAGUE!**

FIGHT!

FIGHT!

FIGHT!

FIGHT!

FIGHT!

FIGHT!

FIGHT!

HA HA! HEE HOH!

GO HOME, STARRO!

AARG!! I'LL BE BACK, KRYPTONIAN!

GO GET HIM, SON.

SO PROUD.

OH, WHAT HAPPENED?

SO... WOOZY.

BOOM!

WITHOUT THEIR MASTER, STARRO'S MINIONS ARE FLEEING INTO SPACE!

NOW TO GET BACK TO EARTH!

SMASH!

PRYM-EL? MY SON?

CREATORS

ART BALTAZAR IS A CARTOONIST MACHINE FROM THE HEART OF CHICAGO! HE DEFINES CARTOONS AND COMICS NOT ONLY AS AN ART STYLE, BUT AS A WAY OF LIFE. CURRENTLY, ART IS THE CREATIVE FORCE BEHIND *THE NEW YORK TIMES* BEST-SELLING, EISNER AWARD-WINNING DC COMICS SERIES TINY TITANS, THE CO-WRITER FOR *BILLY BATSON AND THE MAGIC OF SHAZAM!,* AND CO-CREATOR OF SUPERMAN FAMILY ADVENTURES. ART IS LIVING THE DREAM! HE DRAWS COMICS AND NEVER HAS TO LEAVE THE HOUSE. HE LIVES WITH HIS LOVELY WIFE, ROSE, BIG BOY SONNY, LITTLE BOY GORDON AND LITTLE GIRL AUDREY. RIGHT ON!

ART BALTAZAR

FRANCO

FRANCO AURELIANI, BRONX, NEW YORK, BORN WRITER AND ARTIST, HAS BEEN DRAWING COMICS SINCE HE COULD HOLD A CRAYON. CURRENTLY RESIDING IN UPSTATE NEW YORK WITH HIS WIFE, IVETTE, AND SON, NICOLAS, FRANCO SPENDS MOST OF HIS DAYS IN A BATCAVE-LIKE STUDIO WHERE HE HAS PRODUCED DC'S TINY TITANS COMICS. IN 1995, FRANCO FOUNDED BLINDWOLF STUDIOS, AN INDEPENDENT ART STUDIO WHERE HE AND FELLOW CREATORS CAN CREATE CHILDREN'S COMICS. FRANCO IS THE CREATOR, ARTIST, AND WRITER OF *PATRICK THE WOLF BOY.* WHEN HE'S NOT WRITING AND DRAWING, FRANCO ALSO TEACHES HIGH SCHOOL ART.

GLOSSARY

agenda list of things that need to be done or discussed

design create or build something in a specific way

hologram three-dimensional image made by laser beams

hover remain in one place in the air

introduce bring in a new person, or help two or more people to meet

justice fair action or treatment, or when punishment is given for breaking the law

legion large number of soldiers

minion underling, henchman or follower of an important person or villain

outrageous very shocking or offensive

perpetrator someone who commits a certain act, usually breaking a rule or committing a crime

radar device that uses radio waves to track the location of objects

riddle statement or question that makes you think and that often has a surprising answer

robot machine programmed to do jobs usually performed by a person

VISUAL QUESTIONS AND WRITING PROMPTS

1. WHAT IF BLACK MANTA DIDN'T WANT TO JOIN THE LEGION OF DOOM? WRITE WHAT HAPPENS NEXT IN THIS SCENE.

2. LOOK AGAIN AT THE PANEL BELOW. WHAT DO YOU THINK THE STARFISH DID TO THE JUSTICE LEAGUE?

3. WHY DO YOU THINK BRAINIAC WAITED TO ATTACK THE JUSTICE LEAGUE?

4. WHY WOULD BRAINIAC WANT PRYM-EL TO GROW INTO SUPERMAN PRYME?

READ THEM ALL!